*All children have
a great ambition to read
to themselves...*

*and a sense of achievement when they can do so.
The* **read it yourself** *series has been devised to
satisfy their ambition. Since many children learn
from the Ladybird Key Words Reading Scheme,
these stories have been based to a large extent
on the Key Words List, and the tales chosen are
those with which children are likely to be familiar.*

*The series can of course be used as
supplementary reading for any reading scheme.
The Magic Paintbrush is intended for children
reading up to Book 5c of the Ladybird Reading
Scheme. The following words are additional to
the vocabulary used at that level –*

Liang, poor, lived, town, China, hard,
just, enough, live, paint, money,
paintbrush, could, pictures, flat, stones,
birds, beautiful, people, real, day, teacher,
angry, went, dreaming, old, golden,
careful, magic, next, picked, did, wait,
start, finished, life, flew, amazement,
heard, needed, emperor, ordered, lock,
stables, cold, tie, ladder, escaped, fell,
selling, bumped, under, until, bars, turned,
snake, chased, marry, princess, sailing,
wind, waves

*A list of other titles at the same level will be
found on the back cover.*

The Magic Paintbrush

adapted by Fran Hunia
for easy reading from the traditional tale

illustrated by Martin Aitchison

Ladybird Books Loughborough

Liang was a poor boy who lived in a little town in China. He couldn't go to school as he had to work hard all day. He made just enough money for the things he needed to live on.

There was one thing Liang wanted and that was to paint, but he had no paintbrush, and not enough money to get one.

Liang couldn't paint without a
paintbrush, so he had to make do
with drawing. After work he liked to
sit in the sun and draw pictures on
flat stones.

At home he drew beautiful
pictures of birds and trees and
flowers. People came to look at
Liang's drawings.

"What beautiful pictures!" they
all said. "They look so real!"

Liang was pleased that people
liked his drawings.

As Liang was walking home from work one day, he looked in the window of a school. He saw a teacher painting a picture.

Liang walked into the school and said to the teacher, "I am a poor boy but I do want to paint. Please

could you give me a paintbrush?"

The teacher was angry.

"Go away," he said. "Painting is not for poor boys like you. Get out of my school!"

The teacher went on painting and Liang walked away.

Liang went home. He had his tea and then he went to bed. Soon he was dreaming. He dreamed that an old man was by his bed talking to him. The old man had a golden paintbrush.

"This is for you," he said. "Take it, but be careful what you do with it. It's a magic paintbrush."

The old man put the golden
paintbrush on Liang's bed and
walked away.

The next day, as Liang was getting up to go to work, he saw a golden paintbrush on his bed. He picked it up and looked at it.

"My dream was real!" he said. "The old man *did* give me a paintbrush! Now I can do all the painting I like."

Liang couldn't wait to start
painting. He painted a beautiful bird.

As he finished the picture, the bird came to life. It flew up from the picture and out of the window. Liang looked at it in amazement.

The next thing Liang painted was a little fish. As he finished the picture, the fish came to life, and Liang had to run and put it in some water.

All day Liang went on painting. One after the other his pictures came to life.

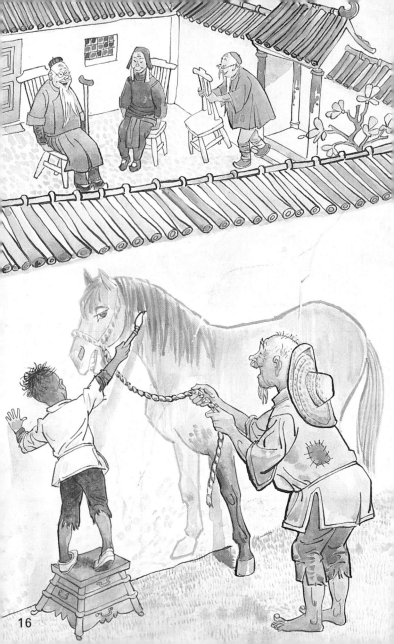

Liang didn't have to go to work after that. He could paint all the things he needed.

Soon people heard about Liang's magic pictures and they came to see him paint. They looked on in amazement as Liang's paintings came to life.

Poor people came to Liang and asked him to paint pictures of things they needed. Liang was pleased to help them. He painted chairs for some old people and a horse for a poor farmer. He went on painting day after day.

Soon the emperor heard about Liang and his magic paintings.

"I must ask that boy to come and paint for me," he said. "He could paint all kinds of things. I could have all the gold I want!"

The emperor ordered his men to go and get Liang. Soon Liang came to talk to the emperor.

"Thank you for asking me to work for you," he said, "but I paint things for poor people. You don't need help."

The emperor was angry that Liang didn't want to work for him.

"I will make you work for me!" he said.

He ordered his men to take Liang away and lock him up in the stables.

"You will be cold out there," said the emperor. "In a day or two you will do as I ask."

Liang was taken away and locked in the stables.

It was cold out in the stables. Liang painted a fire. Next he painted a chair so that he could sit by the fire. Then he painted some good things to eat.

After two days the emperor said, "Liang must be so cold by now that he will be pleased to come and work for me. I will go and talk to him."

The emperor walked out to the stables. He looked in and saw all the things that Liang had painted. He was so angry that he ran into the house and ordered his men to go and tie Liang up.

The emperor's men went out to the stables. They looked for Liang, but he wasn't there. He had painted a ladder and escaped!

The emperor started off up
the ladder after Liang, but he
was a big man, and he soon
fell down again. He ordered
his men to take some horses
and go after Liang. But Liang
saw them coming. He painted
a horse and escaped again.

Now Liang was in danger. The emperor was waiting for him to go home so that he could get him and lock him up again. Liang didn't know what to do. He didn't want to go on painting magic pictures. He wanted to be a real painter.

"I know what I can do," he said.
"I will go on painting, but I won't
finish my pictures. Then they won't
come to life."

Liang went from town to town
painting pictures and selling them.
He was careful not to finish his
paintings, so they didn't come to life.

No one knew who Liang was, and no one knew that his golden paintbrush was magic. Liang was pleased that people liked his pictures. He was pleased to be a real painter now.

31

Then one day Liang painted a
beautiful big bird. He was careful
not to finish the picture. As he was
about to sell it, a man bumped into
him. Some paint fell on the bird and
finished the painting. The bird came
to life and flew up out of the picture.

People looked at the bird in amazement. They saw that Liang's painting had come to life.

"This boy is magic," they said.

A man ran off to see the emperor.

"There is a painter in town who is magic," he said. "He painted a big bird that came to life and flew away."

The emperor knew that it must be Liang. He ordered his men to get Liang and lock him up again.

"Take his magic paintbrush away," said the emperor. "Then he can't paint things to help him to escape."

The emperor's men locked Liang up and took his magic paintbrush. They gave it to the emperor.

"Now I will see if this magic paintbrush will work for me," said the emperor.

He painted some gold. As soon as he had finished the picture he picked up the gold and looked at it. It was real gold!

"It works!" said the emperor.

"Now I can have all the gold I want!"

He went on painting more and more gold until some of it fell down on top of him. His men had to help him out from under the gold.

After that the emperor painted gold bars. One of the gold bars was really big. The emperor picked it up, but it turned into a big snake.

The snake chased the emperor, and his men had to come and help him to get away.

Now the emperor knew that he must have Liang's help to paint the things he wanted.

"I will have to talk Liang into painting for me after all," said the emperor.

He went to talk to Liang.

"Paint pictures for me, and I will let you marry the princess," he said.

Liang didn't want to marry the princess, but he didn't want the emperor to know this.

"Yes," he said. "Give me my paintbrush and I will paint for you."

"What do you want me to paint?" asked Liang.

The emperor ordered him to paint the sea, and Liang did as he said. The sea looked beautiful.

"Now let's have some fish in the sea," said the emperor, and Liang painted all kinds of fish. One by one he picked them up and put them in the sea.

"I want to go sailing," said the
emperor. "Paint me a boat."

Liang painted a beautiful boat
with big red sails. The emperor and

his men went onto the boat and
Liang waited to see what the
emperor wanted next.

"Now paint some wind so that we can go sailing," said the emperor.

Liang painted some wind and the boat started to sail away. Liang painted some big waves. The boat went up and down on the waves.

"Stop painting," ordered the emperor, but Liang went on painting more and more big waves.

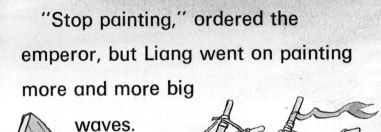

The boat went up and down, up and down.

"Stop, stop! I order you to stop!" said the emperor, but Liang went on painting. He painted more and more wind and waves until the ship went down under the water. Then he walked away.